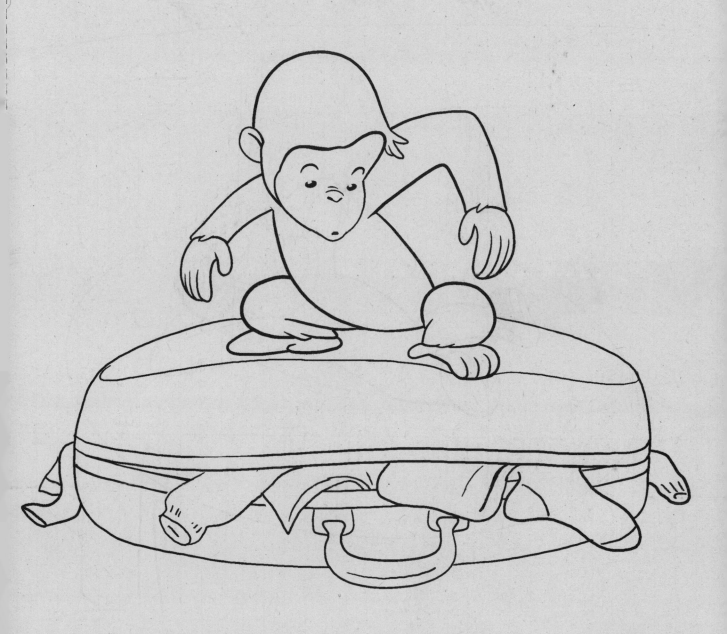

Let's go on vacation—don't pack too much, George!

How about a beach vacation?

Should George take a ski vacation?

A trip to the savanna would be an adventure!

That's a lot of food for a little monkey!

George loves funny movies!

I've brought you a pet, George.

George's fish-eye view.

Oh, no!

Hooray! The circus is in town.

The lion jumps through the hoop.

George gets a ride from a new friend.

George rides a bike on the tightrope.

Whee! Curious George flies high on the trapeze.

Curious George found some clown clothes!

Whee! Follow that monkey!

Around and around we go!

Hello, baby elephant.

**Curious George and his new friend
make beautiful bubbles.**

George likes circus stunts.

Peekaboo! Who is hiding in the hay?

Up, up, and away!

George creates a musical masterpiece!

Thrump-pum-pum!

That sounds great, George!

Be careful of the bees!

Curious George wants to plant a garden.

Roses smell good.

George keeps in touch with his friends.

Don't forget the stamp, George.

George sends the letter on its way.

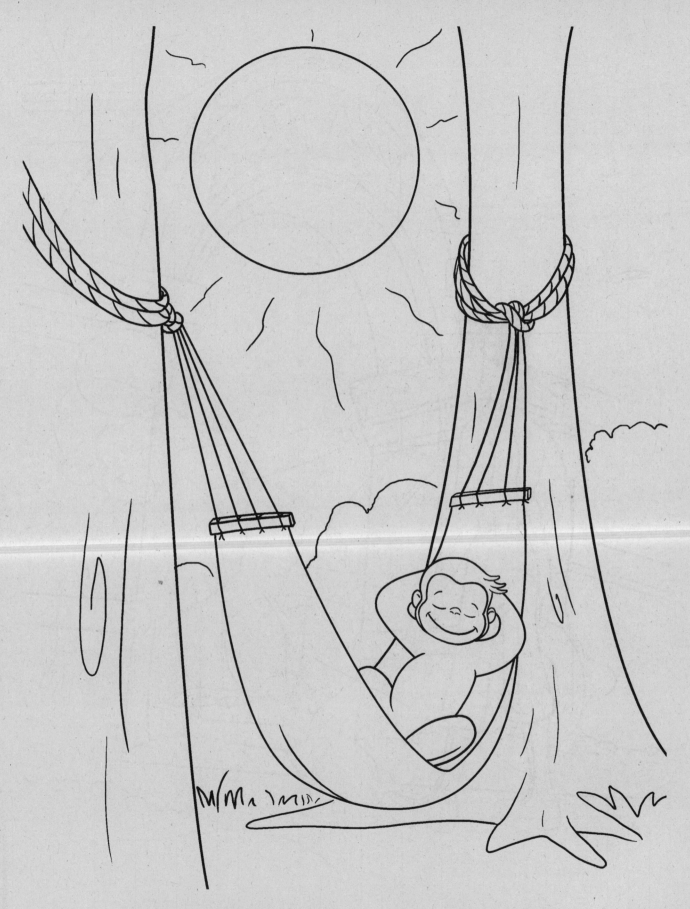

Curious George relaxes on a sunny day.

Let's go to the park!

Curious George loves to fly his kite!

Curious George loves bananas!

This is the perfect day for a picnic.

Party Time!

Those are bouncy balls.

George loves his new rubber duck.

A brand-new fire engine!

George's teddy bear is soft and fuzzy.

Furry friends!

Pajamas can be awfully tricky.

Bedtime stories are the best.

Good night, Curious George.

Arrr! George is dressed up like a pirate.

Yum! George is dressed up like a chef.

Whoosh! Curious George soars above the trees.

Ahoy, Captain George!

George meets a friend by the stream.

George's new friend likes to play leap frog!

There's no wind, so George makes his own!

Play ball!

Let's visit a petting zoo!

Hello, Mr. Turtle.

High five!

A messy masterpiece!

Let's pretend we're in a marching band!

George is going to the amusement park.

What a roller-coaster ride!

What a sticky ride!

George is ready to play!

The man with the yellow hat takes George to the library.

QUIET PLEASE

Shh! No talking in the library.

George loves to read.

The librarian helps George find his favorite book.

George blows beautiful bubbles.

George tries on a good friend's hat.

Park

Curious George and the man
with the yellow hat are best friends.

George Loves to Ride!

Wheee!

Splish! Splash!

Curious George loves to swing.

Look at the beautiful balloons!

Too many balloons!

"Moo!" says the cow.

"Baa!" says the little lamb.

Curious George meets a new friend.

What sweet-smelling flowers!

George picks the perfect present for the man with the yellow hat.

George goes to the aquarium.

The seal balances a ball on his nose.

So does George.

George goes for a ride.

It is nice to read and relax under a shady tree.

Curious George gives this friendly caterpillar a hand.

Aim high, George!

Curious George takes his new pals for a walk.

What interesting music, George.

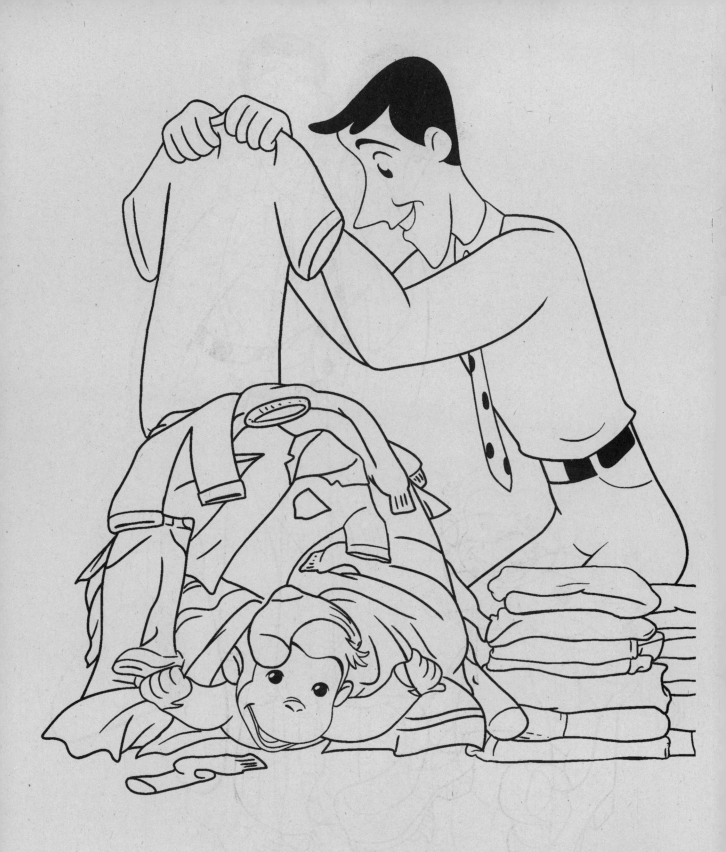

Where's George?

Have you seen my shoes, George?

Nice to meet you, Mr. Bird.